BUSY BOOKS
SERMON NOTES
FOR YOUNG LADIES
AGES TEEN TO ADULT

MADISON & DARLENE SCHACHT

All Scripture is taken from The KJV Bible unless otherwise noted

Busy Books: Sermon Notes for Young Ladies

Time-Warp Wife
Suite 5-1377 Border Street
Winnipeg, Manitoba
R3H ON1

ISBN 978-0-9780262-9-5

Images from Bigstock.com and Thinkstock.com

Find Darlene Schacht on the web here:
Blog: TimeWarpWife.com
Facebook: timewarpwife
Twitter: timewarpwife
Pinterest: timewarpwife

Date
_____

TODAY'S PREACHER

_____

TODAY WE ARE FOCUSING ON THE...

☐ OLD TESTAMENT   ☐ NEW TESTAMENT

Prayer Requests

_____
_____
_____
_____
_____
_____
_____
_____
_____
_____

Today's Sermon is About

_____
_____
_____
_____
_____

Not forsaking the assembling of ourselves together, as the manner of some is; but exhorting one another: and so much the more, as ye see the day approaching.

Hebrews 10:25

1. _____
2. _____
3. _____
4. _____
5. _____

Bible Verses

WHAT CAN I
RESEARCH DEEPER?

_____
_____
_____
_____

Thoughts

_____
_____
_____
_____

SONGS SANG

1. _____
2. _____
3. _____
4. _____
5. _____
6. _____

QUESTIONS

_____
_____
_____
_____
_____
_____
_____

SERMON NOTES...

WHAT IS GOD TELLING ME?

HOW CAN I APPLY THIS TO MY LIFE?

Date
_____

TODAY'S PREACHER
_____

TODAY WE ARE FOCUSING ON THE...

☐ OLD TESTAMENT   ☐ NEW TESTAMENT

Prayer Requests
_____
_____
_____
_____
_____
_____
_____
_____
_____

In all thy ways acknowledge him, and he shall direct thy paths.

Proverbs 3:6

Today's Sermon is About

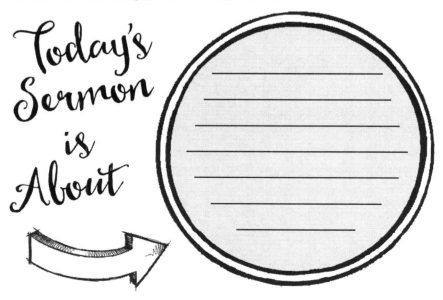

1. _____
2. _____
3. _____
4. _____
5. _____

Bible Verses

WHAT CAN I RESEARCH DEEPER?

_____
_____
_____
_____

Thoughts

_____
_____
_____
_____

SONGS SANG

1. _____
2. _____
3. _____
4. _____
5. _____
6. _____

QUESTIONS

_____
_____
_____
_____
_____
_____

SERMON NOTES...

WHAT IS GOD TELLING ME?

HOW CAN I APPLY THIS TO MY LIFE?

Date

_____

TODAY'S PREACHER

_____

TODAY WE ARE FOCUSING ON THE...

☐ OLD TESTAMENT   ☐ NEW TESTAMENT

Prayer Requests

_____
_____
_____
_____
_____
_____
_____
_____
_____
_____

Blessed be the God and Father of our Lord Jesus Christ, which according to his abundant mercy hath begotten us again unto a lively hope by the resurrection of Jesus Christ from the dead.

1 Peter 1:3

Today's Sermon is About

_____
_____
_____
_____
_____

1. _____
2. _____
3. _____
4. _____
5. _____

Bible Verses

WHAT CAN I
RESEARCH DEEPER?
_____
_____
_____
_____

Thoughts
_____
_____
_____
_____

SONGS SANG

1. _____
2. _____
3. _____
4. _____
5. _____
6. _____

QUESTIONS
_____
_____
_____
_____
_____
_____
_____

SERMON NOTES...

_____
_____
_____
_____
_____
_____
_____
_____
_____
_____

WHAT IS GOD TELLING ME?

_____
_____
_____
_____
_____
_____
_____
_____
_____
_____

HOW CAN I APPLY THIS TO MY LIFE?

_____
_____
_____
_____
_____
_____
_____
_____
_____
_____

Date
_____

TODAY'S PREACHER
_____

TODAY WE ARE FOCUSING ON THE...

☐ OLD TESTAMENT   ☐ NEW TESTAMENT

Prayer Requests
_____
_____
_____
_____
_____
_____
_____
_____
_____
_____
_____

For thou, Lord, wilt bless the righteous; with favour wilt thou compass him as with a shield.

Psalm 5:12

Today's Sermon is About

1. _____
2. _____
3. _____
4. _____
5. _____

Bible Verses

WHAT CAN I RESEARCH DEEPER?

_____
_____
_____
_____

Thoughts

_____
_____
_____
_____

SONGS SANG

1. _____
2. _____
3. _____
4. _____
5. _____
6. _____

QUESTIONS

_____
_____
_____
_____
_____
_____

SERMON NOTES...

WHAT IS GOD TELLING ME?

HOW CAN I APPLY THIS TO MY LIFE?

Date
_____

TODAY'S PREACHER

_____

TODAY WE ARE FOCUSING ON THE...

☐ OLD TESTAMENT   ☐ NEW TESTAMENT

Prayer Requests

For God hath not given us the spirit of fear; but of power, and of love, and of a sound mind.

2 Timothy 1:7

Today's Sermon is About

1. _____
2. _____
3. _____
4. _____
5. _____

Bible Verses

WHAT CAN I RESEARCH DEEPER?

_____
_____
_____
_____

Thoughts

_____
_____
_____
_____

SONGS SANG

1. _____
2. _____
3. _____
4. _____
5. _____
6. _____

QUESTIONS

_____
_____
_____
_____
_____
_____

SERMON NOTES...

WHAT IS GOD TELLING ME?

HOW CAN I APPLY THIS TO MY LIFE?

Date
_____

TODAY'S PREACHER
_____

TODAY WE ARE FOCUSING ON THE...

☐ OLD TESTAMENT ☐ NEW TESTAMENT

Prayer Requests
_____
_____
_____
_____
_____
_____
_____
_____
_____
_____

Keep me as the apple of the eye, hide me under the shadow of thy wings.
Psalm 17:8

Today's Sermon is About

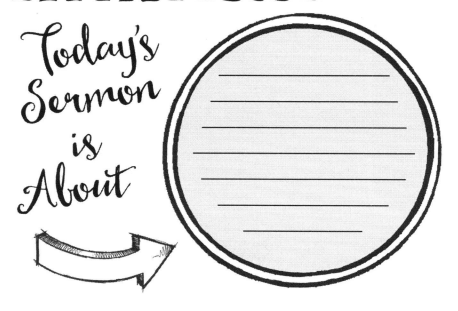

1. _____
2. _____
3. _____
4. _____
5. _____

Bible Verses

WHAT CAN I
RESEARCH DEEPER?

_____
_____
_____
_____

Thoughts

_____
_____
_____
_____

SONGS SANG

1. _____
2. _____
3. _____
4. _____
5. _____
6. _____

QUESTIONS

_____
_____
_____
_____
_____
_____

SERMON NOTES...

WHAT IS GOD TELLING ME?

HOW CAN I APPLY THIS TO MY LIFE?

Date

_____

TODAY'S PREACHER

_____

TODAY WE ARE FOCUSING ON THE...

☐ OLD TESTAMENT   ☐ NEW TESTAMENT

Prayer Requests

_____
_____
_____
_____
_____
_____
_____
_____
_____
_____
_____

Arise; for this matter belongeth unto thee: we also will be with thee: be of good courage, and do it.

Ezra 10:4

Today's Sermon is About

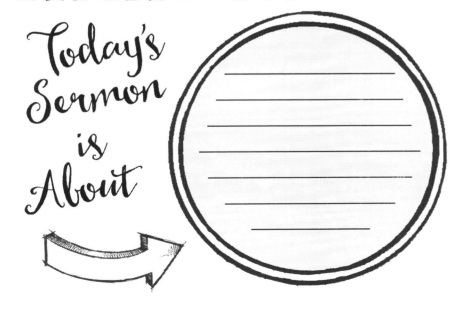

1. _____
2. _____
3. _____
4. _____
5. _____

Bible Verses

WHAT CAN I
RESEARCH DEEPER?

_____
_____
_____
_____

Thoughts

_____
_____
_____
_____

SONGS SANG

1. _____
2. _____
3. _____
4. _____
5. _____
6. _____

QUESTIONS

_____
_____
_____
_____
_____
_____

SERMON NOTES...

WHAT IS GOD TELLING ME?

HOW CAN I APPLY THIS TO MY LIFE?

Date

_____

TODAY'S PREACHER

_____

TODAY WE ARE FOCUSING ON THE...

☐ OLD TESTAMENT ☐ NEW TESTAMENT

Prayer Requests

_____
_____
_____
_____
_____
_____
_____
_____
_____
_____

He that saith he abideth in him ought himself also so to walk, even as he walked.

1 John 2:6

Today's Sermon is About

1. _____
2. _____
3. _____
4. _____
5. _____

Bible Verses

WHAT CAN I
RESEARCH DEEPER?
_____
_____
_____
_____

Thoughts
_____
_____
_____
_____

SONGS SANG

1. _____
2. _____
3. _____
4. _____
5. _____
6. _____

QUESTIONS
_____
_____
_____
_____
_____
_____

SERMON NOTES...

WHAT IS GOD TELLING ME?

HOW CAN I APPLY THIS TO MY LIFE?

Date
_____

TODAY'S PREACHER

_____

TODAY WE ARE FOCUSING ON THE...

☐ OLD TESTAMENT   ☐ NEW TESTAMENT

Prayer Requests

_____
_____
_____
_____
_____
_____
_____
_____
_____
_____
_____

As soon as Jesus
heard the word
that was spoken,
he saith unto the
ruler of the
synagogue,
Be not afraid,
only believe.

Mark 5:36

Today's
Sermon
is
About

_____
_____
_____
_____
_____

1. _____
2. _____
3. _____
4. _____
5. _____

Bible Verses

WHAT CAN I RESEARCH DEEPER?

_____
_____
_____
_____

Thoughts

_____
_____
_____
_____

SONGS SANG

1. _____
2. _____
3. _____
4. _____
5. _____
6. _____

QUESTIONS

_____
_____
_____
_____
_____
_____

SERMON NOTES...

_____
_____
_____
_____
_____
_____
_____

WHAT IS GOD TELLING ME?

_____
_____
_____
_____
_____
_____
_____
_____

HOW CAN I APPLY THIS TO MY LIFE?

_____
_____
_____
_____
_____
_____
_____
_____

Date

_____

TODAY'S PREACHER

_____

TODAY WE ARE FOCUSING ON THE...

☐ OLD TESTAMENT ☐ NEW TESTAMENT

Prayer Requests

_____
_____
_____
_____
_____
_____
_____
_____
_____
_____

My help cometh from the Lord, which made heaven and earth.

Psalms 121:2

Today's Sermon is About

1. _____
2. _____
3. _____
4. _____
5. _____

Bible Verses

WHAT CAN I
RESEARCH DEEPER?

_____
_____
_____
_____

Thoughts

_____
_____
_____
_____

SONGS SANG

1. _____
2. _____
3. _____
4. _____
5. _____
6. _____

QUESTIONS

_____
_____
_____
_____
_____

SERMON NOTES...

_____
_____
_____
_____
_____
_____
_____
_____

WHAT IS GOD TELLING ME?

_____
_____
_____
_____
_____
_____
_____
_____
_____

HOW CAN I APPLY THIS TO MY LIFE?

_____
_____
_____
_____
_____
_____
_____
_____

Date

_____

TODAY'S PREACHER

_____

TODAY WE ARE FOCUSING ON THE...

☐ OLD TESTAMENT   ☐ NEW TESTAMENT

Prayer Requests

_____
_____
_____
_____
_____
_____
_____
_____
_____
_____
_____

He will deliver his soul from going into the pit, and his life shall see the light.

Job. 33:28

Today's Sermon is About

_____
_____
_____
_____
_____

1. _____
2. _____
3. _____
4. _____
5. _____

Bible Verses

WHAT CAN I
RESEARCH DEEPER?
_____
_____
_____
_____

Thoughts
_____
_____
_____
_____

SONGS SANG

1. _____
2. _____
3. _____
4. _____
5. _____
6. _____

QUESTIONS
_____
_____
_____
_____
_____
_____

SERMON NOTES...

WHAT IS GOD TELLING ME?

HOW CAN I APPLY THIS TO MY LIFE?

Date

_____

TODAY'S PREACHER

_____

TODAY WE ARE FOCUSING ON THE...

☐ OLD TESTAMENT ☐ NEW TESTAMENT

Prayer Requests

_____
_____
_____
_____
_____
_____
_____
_____
_____
_____
_____

Let your light so shine before men, that they may see your good works, and glorify your Father which is in heaven.

Matthew 5:16

Today's Sermon is About

1. _____
2. _____
3. _____
4. _____
5. _____

Bible Verses

WHAT CAN I RESEARCH DEEPER?

_____
_____
_____
_____

Thoughts

_____
_____
_____
_____

SONGS SANG

1. _____
2. _____
3. _____
4. _____
5. _____
6. _____

QUESTIONS

_____
_____
_____
_____
_____
_____

SERMON NOTES...

WHAT IS GOD TELLING ME?

HOW CAN I APPLY THIS TO MY LIFE?

Date
_____

TODAY'S PREACHER
_____

TODAY WE ARE FOCUSING ON THE...

☐ OLD TESTAMENT　　☐ NEW TESTAMENT

Prayer Requests

_____
_____
_____
_____
_____
_____
_____
_____
_____
_____
_____

For the mountains shall depart, and the hills be removed; but my kindness shall not depart from thee, neither shall the covenant of my peace be removed, saith the Lord that hath mercy on thee.

Isaiah 54:10

Today's Sermon is About

1. _____
2. _____
3. _____
4. _____
5. _____

Bible Verses

WHAT CAN I
RESEARCH DEEPER?

_____
_____
_____
_____

Thoughts

_____
_____
_____
_____

SONGS SANG

1. _____
2. _____
3. _____
4. _____
5. _____
6. _____

QUESTIONS

_____
_____
_____
_____
_____
_____
_____

SERMON NOTES...

WHAT IS GOD TELLING ME?

HOW CAN I APPLY THIS TO MY LIFE?

Date

_____

TODAY'S PREACHER

_____

TODAY WE ARE FOCUSING ON THE...

☐ OLD TESTAMENT   ☐ NEW TESTAMENT

Prayer Requests

_____
_____
_____
_____
_____
_____
_____
_____
_____
_____

With all lowliness and meekness, with longsuffering, forbearing one another in love.

Ephesians 4:2

Today's Sermon is About

1. _____
2. _____
3. _____
4. _____
5. _____

Bible Verses

WHAT CAN I
RESEARCH DEEPER?

_____
_____
_____
_____

Thoughts

_____
_____
_____
_____

SONGS SANG

1. _____
2. _____
3. _____
4. _____
5. _____
6. _____

QUESTIONS

_____
_____
_____
_____
_____
_____

SERMON NOTES...

WHAT IS GOD TELLING ME?

HOW CAN I APPLY THIS TO MY LIFE?

Date

_____

TODAY'S PREACHER

_____

TODAY WE ARE FOCUSING ON THE...

☐ OLD TESTAMENT   ☐ NEW TESTAMENT

Prayer Requests

_____
_____
_____
_____
_____
_____
_____
_____
_____
_____
_____

And he must needs go through Samaria

John 4:4

Today's Sermon is About

_____
_____
_____
_____
_____

1. _____
2. _____
3. _____
4. _____
5. _____

Bible Verses

WHAT CAN I
RESEARCH DEEPER?

Thoughts

SONGS SANG

1. _____
2. _____
3. _____
4. _____
5. _____
6. _____

QUESTIONS

SERMON NOTES...

WHAT IS GOD TELLING ME?

HOW CAN I APPLY THIS TO MY LIFE?

Date

_____

TODAY'S PREACHER

_____

TODAY WE ARE FOCUSING ON THE...

☐ OLD TESTAMENT ☐ NEW TESTAMENT

Prayer Requests

_____
_____
_____
_____
_____
_____
_____
_____
_____
_____

Have not I commanded thee? Be strong and of a good courage; be not afraid, neither be thou dismayed: for the Lord thy God is with thee whithersoever thou goest.

Joshua 1:9

Today's Sermon is About

_____
_____
_____
_____
_____

1. _____
2. _____
3. _____
4. _____
5. _____

Bible Verses

WHAT CAN I
RESEARCH DEEPER?

Thoughts

SONGS SANG

1. _____
2. _____
3. _____
4. _____
5. _____
6. _____

QUESTIONS

SERMON NOTES...

WHAT IS GOD TELLING ME?

HOW CAN I APPLY THIS TO MY LIFE?

Date

_____

TODAY'S PREACHER

_____

TODAY WE ARE FOCUSING ON THE...

☐ OLD TESTAMENT   ☐ NEW TESTAMENT

Prayer Requests

_____
_____
_____
_____
_____
_____
_____
_____
_____
_____
_____
_____

Beareth all things,
believeth all things,
hopeth all things,
endureth all things.
1 Corinthians 13:7

Today's Sermon is About

1. _____
2. _____
3. _____
4. _____
5. _____

Bible Verses

WHAT CAN I
RESEARCH DEEPER?

_____
_____
_____
_____

Thoughts

_____
_____
_____
_____

SONGS SANG

1. _____
2. _____
3. _____
4. _____
5. _____
6. _____

QUESTIONS

_____
_____
_____
_____
_____
_____

SERMON NOTES...

_____
_____
_____
_____
_____
_____
_____
_____

WHAT IS GOD TELLING ME?

_____
_____
_____
_____
_____
_____
_____
_____

HOW CAN I APPLY THIS TO MY LIFE?

_____
_____
_____
_____
_____
_____
_____
_____
_____

Date
_____

TODAY'S PREACHER

_____

TODAY WE ARE FOCUSING ON THE...

☐ OLD TESTAMENT   ☐ NEW TESTAMENT

Prayer Requests

_____
_____
_____
_____
_____
_____
_____
_____
_____
_____

For I know the thoughts that I think toward you, saith the Lord, thoughts of peace, and not of evil, to give you an expected end.

Jeremiah 29:11

Today's Sermon is About

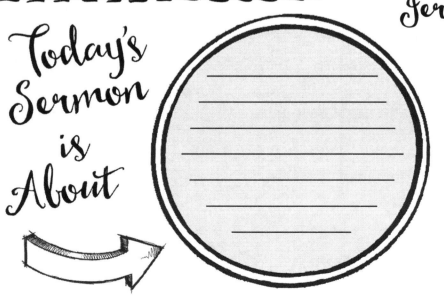

1. _____
2. _____
3. _____
4. _____
5. _____

Bible Verses

WHAT CAN I
RESEARCH DEEPER?
_____
_____
_____
_____

Thoughts
_____
_____
_____
_____

SONGS SANG

1. _____
2. _____
3. _____
4. _____
5. _____
6. _____

QUESTIONS
_____
_____
_____
_____
_____
_____

SERMON NOTES...

WHAT IS GOD TELLING ME?

HOW CAN I APPLY THIS TO MY LIFE?

Date

_____

TODAY'S PREACHER

_____

TODAY WE ARE FOCUSING ON THE...

☐ OLD TESTAMENT   ☐ NEW TESTAMENT

Prayer Requests

_____
_____
_____
_____
_____
_____
_____
_____
_____
_____

Epaphras, who is one of you, a servant of Christ, saluteth you, always labouring fervently for you in prayers, that ye may stand perfect and complete in all the will of God.

Colossians 4:12

Today's Sermon is About

_____
_____
_____
_____

1. _____
2. _____
3. _____
4. _____
5. _____

Bible Verses

WHAT CAN I
RESEARCH DEEPER?

_____
_____
_____
_____

Thoughts

_____
_____
_____
_____
_____

SONGS SANG

1. _____
2. _____
3. _____
4. _____
5. _____
6. _____

QUESTIONS

_____
_____
_____
_____
_____
_____

SERMON NOTES...

WHAT IS GOD TELLING ME?

HOW CAN I APPLY THIS TO MY LIFE?

Date
_____

TODAY'S PREACHER

_____

TODAY WE ARE FOCUSING ON THE...

☐ OLD TESTAMENT   ☐ NEW TESTAMENT

Prayer Requests
_____
_____
_____
_____
_____
_____
_____
_____
_____

Ye are the light of the world. A city that is set on an hill cannot be hid.

Matthew 5:14

Today's Sermon is About

1. _____
2. _____
3. _____
4. _____
5. _____

Bible Verses

WHAT CAN I RESEARCH DEEPER?

_____
_____
_____
_____

Thoughts

_____
_____
_____
_____

SONGS SANG

1. _____
2. _____
3. _____
4. _____
5. _____
6. _____

QUESTIONS

_____
_____
_____
_____
_____
_____

SERMON NOTES...

WHAT IS GOD TELLING ME?

HOW CAN I APPLY THIS TO MY LIFE?

Date

_____

TODAY'S PREACHER

_____

TODAY WE ARE FOCUSING ON THE...

☐ OLD TESTAMENT   ☐ NEW TESTAMENT

Prayer Requests

_____
_____
_____
_____
_____
_____
_____
_____
_____
_____

And they that be wise shall shine as the brightness of the firmament; and they that turn many to righteousness as the stars for ever and ever.

Daniel 12:3

Today's Sermon is About

1. _____
2. _____
3. _____
4. _____
5. _____

Bible Verses

WHAT CAN I RESEARCH DEEPER?

_____
_____
_____
_____

Thoughts

_____
_____
_____
_____

SONGS SANG

1. _____
2. _____
3. _____
4. _____
5. _____
6. _____

QUESTIONS

_____
_____
_____
_____
_____
_____

SERMON NOTES...

WHAT IS GOD TELLING ME?

HOW CAN I APPLY THIS TO MY LIFE?

Date

_____

TODAY'S PREACHER

_____

TODAY WE ARE FOCUSING ON THE...

☐ OLD TESTAMENT   ☐ NEW TESTAMENT

Prayer Requests

_____
_____
_____
_____
_____
_____
_____
_____
_____

I cried unto the Lord with my voice, and he heard me out of his holy hill. Selah.

Psalm 3:4

Today's Sermon is About

_____
_____
_____
_____
_____

1. _____
2. _____
3. _____
4. _____
5. _____

Bible Verses

WHAT CAN I RESEARCH DEEPER?

_____
_____
_____
_____

Thoughts

_____
_____
_____
_____

SONGS SANG

1. _____
2. _____
3. _____
4. _____
5. _____
6. _____

QUESTIONS

_____
_____
_____
_____
_____
_____

SERMON NOTES...

WHAT IS GOD TELLING ME?

HOW CAN I APPLY THIS TO MY LIFE?

Date
_____

TODAY'S PREACHER

_____

TODAY WE ARE FOCUSING ON THE...

☐ OLD TESTAMENT   ☐ NEW TESTAMENT

Prayer Requests
_____
_____
_____
_____
_____
_____
_____
_____
_____
_____
_____

Jesus answered and said unto him, What I do thou knowest not now; but thou shalt know hereafter.

John 13:7

Today's Sermon is About

1. _____
2. _____
3. _____
4. _____
5. _____

Bible Verses

WHAT CAN I
RESEARCH DEEPER?

_____
_____
_____
_____

Thoughts

_____
_____
_____
_____

SONGS SANG

1. _____
2. _____
3. _____
4. _____
5. _____
6. _____

QUESTIONS

_____
_____
_____
_____
_____
_____
_____

SERMON NOTES...

WHAT IS GOD TELLING ME?

HOW CAN I APPLY THIS TO MY LIFE?

Date

_____

TODAY'S PREACHER

_____

TODAY WE ARE FOCUSING ON THE...

☐ OLD TESTAMENT   ☐ NEW TESTAMENT

Prayer Requests

_____
_____
_____
_____
_____
_____
_____
_____
_____
_____

Blessed is the man that endureth temptation: for when he is tried, he shall receive the crown of life, which the Lord hath promised to them that love him.

James 1:12

Today's Sermon is About

_____
_____
_____
_____
_____
_____

1. _____
2. _____
3. _____
4. _____
5. _____

Bible Verses

WHAT CAN I RESEARCH DEEPER?

_____
_____
_____
_____

Thoughts

_____
_____
_____
_____

SONGS SANG

1. _____
2. _____
3. _____
4. _____
5. _____
6. _____

QUESTIONS

_____
_____
_____
_____
_____
_____
_____

SERMON NOTES...

WHAT IS GOD TELLING ME?

HOW CAN I APPLY THIS TO MY LIFE?

Date
_____

TODAY'S PREACHER

_____

TODAY WE ARE FOCUSING ON THE...

☐ OLD TESTAMENT   ☐ NEW TESTAMENT

Prayer Requests

_____
_____
_____
_____
_____
_____
_____
_____
_____
_____
_____

Then he said unto them, Go your way, eat the fat, and drink the sweet, and send portions unto them for whom nothing is prepared: for this day is holy unto our Lord: neither be ye sorry; for the joy of the Lord is your strength.

Nehemiah 8:10

Today's Sermon is About

_____
_____
_____
_____
_____

1. _____
2. _____
3. _____
4. _____
5. _____

Bible Verses

WHAT CAN I
RESEARCH DEEPER?
_____
_____
_____
_____

Thoughts
_____
_____
_____
_____

SONGS SANG
1. _____
2. _____
3. _____
4. _____
5. _____
6. _____

QUESTIONS
_____
_____
_____
_____
_____
_____

SERMON NOTES...

WHAT IS GOD TELLING ME?

HOW CAN I APPLY THIS TO MY LIFE?

Date
_____

TODAY'S PREACHER
_____

TODAY WE ARE FOCUSING ON THE...

☐ OLD TESTAMENT   ☐ NEW TESTAMENT

Prayer Requests
_____
_____
_____
_____
_____
_____
_____
_____
_____

What shall we then say to these things? If God be for us, who can be against us?

Romans 8:31

Today's Sermon is About

1. _____
2. _____
3. _____
4. _____
5. _____

Bible Verses

WHAT CAN I RESEARCH DEEPER?

_____
_____
_____
_____

Thoughts

_____
_____
_____
_____

SONGS SANG

1. _____
2. _____
3. _____
4. _____
5. _____
6. _____

QUESTIONS

_____
_____
_____
_____
_____
_____
_____
_____

SERMON NOTES...

WHAT IS GOD TELLING ME?

HOW CAN I APPLY THIS TO MY LIFE?

Date

_____

TODAY'S PREACHER

_____

TODAY WE ARE FOCUSING ON THE...

☐ OLD TESTAMENT ☐ NEW TESTAMENT

Prayer Requests

_____
_____
_____
_____
_____
_____
_____
_____
_____
_____
_____

He only is my rock and my salvation: he is my defence; I shall not be moved.

Psalm 62:6

Today's Sermon is About

_____
_____
_____
_____
_____

1. _____
2. _____
3. _____
4. _____
5. _____

Bible Verses

WHAT CAN I RESEARCH DEEPER?

_____
_____
_____
_____

Thoughts

_____
_____
_____
_____

SONGS SANG

1. _____
2. _____
3. _____
4. _____
5. _____
6. _____

QUESTIONS

_____
_____
_____
_____
_____
_____

SERMON NOTES...

WHAT IS GOD TELLING ME?

HOW CAN I APPLY THIS TO MY LIFE?

Date

_____

TODAY'S PREACHER

_____

TODAY WE ARE FOCUSING ON THE...

☐ OLD TESTAMENT   ☐ NEW TESTAMENT

Prayer Requests

_____
_____
_____
_____
_____
_____
_____
_____
_____
_____

As the hart panteth after the water brooks, so panteth my soul after thee, O God.

Psalm 42:1

Today's Sermon is About

1. _____
2. _____
3. _____
4. _____
5. _____

Bible Verses

WHAT CAN I RESEARCH DEEPER?

_____
_____
_____
_____

Thoughts

_____
_____
_____
_____

SONGS SANG

1. _____
2. _____
3. _____
4. _____
5. _____
6. _____

QUESTIONS

_____
_____
_____
_____
_____
_____

SERMON NOTES...

WHAT IS GOD TELLING ME?

HOW CAN I APPLY THIS TO MY LIFE?

Date

_____

TODAY'S PREACHER

_____

TODAY WE ARE FOCUSING ON THE...

☐ OLD TESTAMENT   ☐ NEW TESTAMENT

Prayer Requests

_____
_____
_____
_____
_____
_____
_____
_____
_____
_____
_____

Pleasant words are as an honeycomb, sweet to the soul and health to the bones.

Proverbs 16:24

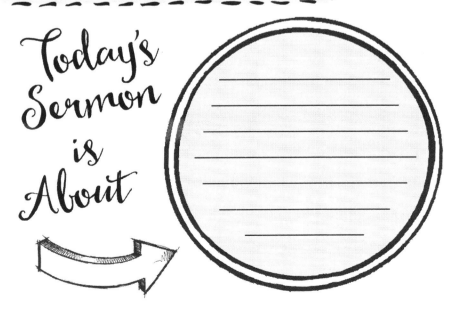

Today's Sermon is About

_____
_____
_____
_____
_____

1. _____
2. _____
3. _____
4. _____
5. _____

Bible Verses

WHAT CAN I RESEARCH DEEPER?

_____
_____
_____
_____

Thoughts

_____
_____
_____
_____

SONGS SANG

1. _____
2. _____
3. _____
4. _____
5. _____
6. _____

QUESTIONS

_____
_____
_____
_____
_____
_____

SERMON NOTES...

WHAT IS GOD TELLING ME?

HOW CAN I APPLY THIS TO MY LIFE?

Date
_____

TODAY'S PREACHER
_____

TODAY WE ARE FOCUSING ON THE...

☐ OLD TESTAMENT ☐ NEW TESTAMENT

Prayer Requests
_____
_____
_____
_____
_____
_____
_____
_____
_____
_____

She openeth her mouth with wisdom; and in her tongue is the law of kindness.

Proverbs 31:26

Today's Sermon is About

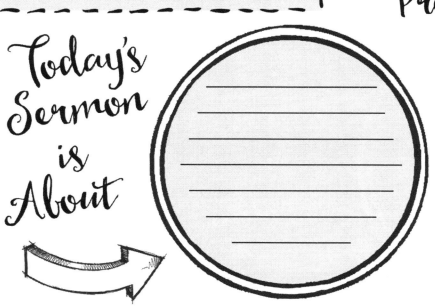

1. _____
2. _____
3. _____
4. _____
5. _____

Bible Verses

WHAT CAN I
RESEARCH DEEPER?
_____
_____
_____
_____

Thoughts
_____
_____
_____
_____

SONGS SANG

1. _____
2. _____
3. _____
4. _____
5. _____
6. _____

QUESTIONS
_____
_____
_____
_____
_____
_____
_____

SERMON NOTES...

WHAT IS GOD TELLING ME?

HOW CAN I APPLY THIS TO MY LIFE?

Date
_____

TODAY'S PREACHER

_____

TODAY WE ARE FOCUSING ON THE...

☐ OLD TESTAMENT ☐ NEW TESTAMENT

Prayer Requests

_____
_____
_____
_____
_____
_____
_____
_____
_____
_____
_____

Who I am in Christ matters more than what I think or what other people tell me about myself.

Colossians 3:1-4

Today's Sermon is About

_____
_____
_____
_____
_____

1. _____
2. _____
3. _____
4. _____
5. _____

Bible Verses

WHAT CAN I RESEARCH DEEPER?

_____
_____
_____
_____

Thoughts

_____
_____
_____
_____

SONGS SANG

1. _____
2. _____
3. _____
4. _____
5. _____
6. _____

QUESTIONS

_____
_____
_____
_____
_____
_____

SERMON NOTES...

WHAT IS GOD TELLING ME?

HOW CAN I APPLY THIS TO MY LIFE?

Date

_____

TODAY'S PREACHER

_____

TODAY WE ARE FOCUSING ON THE...

☐ OLD TESTAMENT   ☐ NEW TESTAMENT

Prayer Requests

_____
_____
_____
_____
_____
_____
_____
_____
_____
_____

The Lord also will be a refuge for the oppressed, a refuge in times of trouble.

Psalm 9:9

Today's Sermon is About

1. _____
2. _____
3. _____
4. _____
5. _____

Bible Verses

WHAT CAN I RESEARCH DEEPER?

_____
_____
_____
_____

Thoughts

_____
_____
_____
_____

SONGS SANG

1. _____
2. _____
3. _____
4. _____
5. _____
6. _____

QUESTIONS

_____
_____
_____
_____
_____

SERMON NOTES...

WHAT IS GOD TELLING ME?

HOW CAN I APPLY THIS TO MY LIFE?

Date
_____

TODAY'S PREACHER
_____

TODAY WE ARE FOCUSING ON THE...

☐ OLD TESTAMENT ☐ NEW TESTAMENT

Prayer Requests

_____
_____
_____
_____
_____
_____
_____
_____
_____
_____
_____

And blessed is she that believed: for there shall be a performance of those things which were told her from the Lord.

Luke 1:45

Today's Sermon is About

_____
_____
_____
_____
_____

1. _____
2. _____
3. _____
4. _____
5. _____

Bible Verses

WHAT CAN I RESEARCH DEEPER?

_____
_____
_____
_____

Thoughts

_____
_____
_____
_____

SONGS SANG

1. _____
2. _____
3. _____
4. _____
5. _____
6. _____

QUESTIONS

_____
_____
_____
_____
_____
_____

SERMON NOTES...

WHAT IS GOD TELLING ME?

HOW CAN I APPLY THIS TO MY LIFE?

Date

_____

TODAY'S PREACHER

_____

TODAY WE ARE FOCUSING ON THE...

☐ OLD TESTAMENT   ☐ NEW TESTAMENT

Prayer Requests

_____
_____
_____
_____
_____
_____
_____
_____
_____

Set your affection on things above, not on things on the earth.

Colossians 3:2

Today's Sermon is About

1.
2.
3.
4.
5.

Bible Verses

WHAT CAN I RESEARCH DEEPER?

Thoughts

SONGS SANG

1.
2.
3.
4.
5.
6.

QUESTIONS

SERMON NOTES...

WHAT IS GOD TELLING ME?

HOW CAN I APPLY THIS TO MY LIFE?

Date

_____

TODAY'S PREACHER

_____

TODAY WE ARE FOCUSING ON THE...

☐ OLD TESTAMENT   ☐ NEW TESTAMENT

Prayer Requests

_____
_____
_____
_____
_____
_____
_____
_____
_____
_____

Let your conversation be without covetousness; and be content with such things as ye have: for he hath said, I will never leave thee, nor forsake thee.

Hebrews 13:5

Today's Sermon is About

_____
_____
_____
_____
_____

1. _____
2. _____
3. _____
4. _____
5. _____

Bible Verses

WHAT CAN I RESEARCH DEEPER?

_____
_____
_____
_____

Thoughts

_____
_____
_____
_____

SONGS SANG

1. _____
2. _____
3. _____
4. _____
5. _____
6. _____

QUESTIONS

_____
_____
_____
_____
_____

SERMON NOTES...

WHAT IS GOD TELLING ME?

HOW CAN I APPLY THIS TO MY LIFE?

Date

_____

TODAY'S PREACHER

_____

TODAY WE ARE FOCUSING ON THE...

☐ OLD TESTAMENT   ☐ NEW TESTAMENT

Prayer Requests

_____
_____
_____
_____
_____
_____
_____
_____
_____
_____

Fear not:
for I am with thee:
I will bring thy
seed from the east,
and gather thee
from the west.

Isaiah 43:5

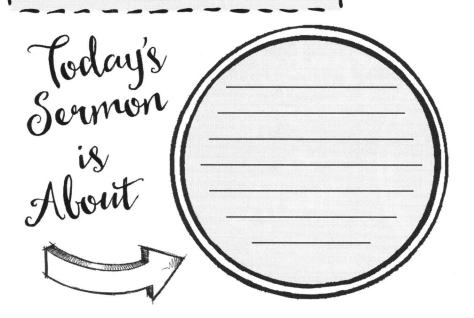

Today's Sermon is About

_____
_____
_____
_____
_____

1. _____
2. _____
3. _____
4. _____
5. _____

Bible Verses

WHAT CAN I RESEARCH DEEPER?

_____
_____
_____
_____

Thoughts

_____
_____
_____
_____

SONGS SANG

1. _____
2. _____
3. _____
4. _____
5. _____
6. _____

QUESTIONS

_____
_____
_____
_____
_____

SERMON NOTES...

WHAT IS GOD TELLING ME?

HOW CAN I APPLY THIS TO MY LIFE?

Date

_____

TODAY'S PREACHER

_____

TODAY WE ARE FOCUSING ON THE...

☐ OLD TESTAMENT   ☐ NEW TESTAMENT

Prayer Requests

_____
_____
_____
_____
_____
_____
_____
_____
_____
_____
_____

Draw nigh to God, and he will draw nigh to you. Cleanse your hands, ye sinners; and purify your hearts, ye double minded.

James 4:8

Today's Sermon is About

1. _____
2. _____
3. _____
4. _____
5. _____

Bible Verses

WHAT CAN I RESEARCH DEEPER?

_____
_____
_____
_____

Thoughts

_____
_____
_____
_____

SONGS SANG

1. _____
2. _____
3. _____
4. _____
5. _____
6. _____

QUESTIONS

_____
_____
_____
_____
_____
_____

SERMON NOTES...

WHAT IS GOD TELLING ME?

HOW CAN I APPLY
THIS TO MY LIFE?

Date

_____

TODAY'S PREACHER

_____

TODAY WE ARE FOCUSING ON THE...

☐ OLD TESTAMENT   ☐ NEW TESTAMENT

Prayer Requests

_____
_____
_____
_____
_____
_____
_____
_____
_____
_____
_____

Rest in the Lord, and wait patiently for him: fret not thyself because of him who prospereth in his way, because of the man who bringeth wicked devices to pass.

Psalm 37:7

Today's Sermon is About

1. _____
2. _____
3. _____
4. _____
5. _____

Bible Verses

WHAT CAN I RESEARCH DEEPER?

_____
_____
_____
_____

Thoughts

_____
_____
_____
_____

SONGS SANG

1. _____
2. _____
3. _____
4. _____
5. _____
6. _____

QUESTIONS

_____
_____
_____
_____
_____
_____

SERMON NOTES...

WHAT IS GOD TELLING ME?

HOW CAN I APPLY THIS TO MY LIFE?

Date
_____

TODAY'S PREACHER

_____

TODAY WE ARE FOCUSING ON THE...

☐ OLD TESTAMENT ☐ NEW TESTAMENT

Prayer Requests

_____
_____
_____
_____
_____
_____
_____
_____
_____
_____
_____

Wherefore they are no more twain, but one flesh. What therefore God hath joined together, let not man put asunder.

Matthew 19:6

Today's Sermon is About

1. _____
2. _____
3. _____
4. _____
5. _____

Bible Verses

WHAT CAN I RESEARCH DEEPER?

_____
_____
_____
_____

Thoughts

_____
_____
_____
_____

SONGS SANG

1. _____
2. _____
3. _____
4. _____
5. _____
6. _____

QUESTIONS

_____
_____
_____
_____
_____
_____

SERMON NOTES...

WHAT IS GOD TELLING ME?

HOW CAN I APPLY THIS TO MY LIFE?

Date

_____

TODAY'S PREACHER

_____

TODAY WE ARE FOCUSING ON THE...

☐ OLD TESTAMENT   ☐ NEW TESTAMENT

Prayer Requests

_____
_____
_____
_____
_____
_____
_____
_____
_____
_____

There are many devices in a man's heart; nevertheless the counsel of the Lord, that shall stand.

Proverbs 19:21

Today's Sermon is About

_____
_____
_____
_____
_____

1. _____
2. _____
3. _____
4. _____
5. _____

Bible Verses

WHAT CAN I RESEARCH DEEPER?

_____
_____
_____
_____

Thoughts

_____
_____
_____
_____

SONGS SANG

1. _____
2. _____
3. _____
4. _____
5. _____
6. _____

QUESTIONS

_____
_____
_____
_____
_____
_____
_____

SERMON NOTES...

WHAT IS GOD TELLING ME?

HOW CAN I APPLY THIS TO MY LIFE?

Date
_____

TODAY'S PREACHER

_____

TODAY WE ARE FOCUSING ON THE...

☐ OLD TESTAMENT   ☐ NEW TESTAMENT

Prayer Requests

_____
_____
_____
_____
_____
_____
_____
_____
_____
_____
_____

A seed shall serve him; it shall be accounted to the Lord for a generation. Psalm 22:30

Today's Sermon is About

1. _____
2. _____
3. _____
4. _____
5. _____

Bible Verses

WHAT CAN I RESEARCH DEEPER?

_____
_____
_____
_____

Thoughts

_____
_____
_____
_____

SONGS SANG

1. _____
2. _____
3. _____
4. _____
5. _____
6. _____

QUESTIONS

_____
_____
_____
_____
_____
_____

SERMON NOTES...

WHAT IS GOD TELLING ME?

HOW CAN I APPLY
THIS TO MY LIFE?

Date

_____

TODAY'S PREACHER

_____

TODAY WE ARE FOCUSING ON THE...

☐ OLD TESTAMENT   ☐ NEW TESTAMENT

Prayer Requests

_____
_____
_____
_____
_____
_____
_____
_____
_____
_____

Then shalt thou call, and the Lord shall answer; thou shalt cry, and he shall say, Here I am. If thou take away from the midst of thee the yoke, the putting forth of the finger, and speaking vanity.

Isaiah 58:9

Today's Sermon is About

_____
_____
_____
_____
_____

1. _____
2. _____
3. _____
4. _____
5. _____

Bible Verses

WHAT CAN I RESEARCH DEEPER?

_____
_____
_____
_____

Thoughts

_____
_____
_____
_____

SONGS SANG

1. _____
2. _____
3. _____
4. _____
5. _____
6. _____

QUESTIONS

_____
_____
_____
_____
_____
_____
_____

SERMON NOTES...

WHAT IS GOD TELLING ME?

HOW CAN I APPLY THIS TO MY LIFE?

Date
_____

TODAY'S PREACHER

_____

TODAY WE ARE FOCUSING ON THE...

☐ OLD TESTAMENT ☐ NEW TESTAMENT

Prayer Requests

_____
_____
_____
_____
_____
_____
_____
_____
_____

And Ruth said, Intreat me not to leave thee, or to return from following after thee: for whither thou goest, I will go; and where thou lodgest, I will lodge: thy people shall be my people, and thy God my God.

Ruth 1:16

Today's Sermon is About

_____
_____
_____
_____
_____

1. _____
2. _____
3. _____
4. _____
5. _____

Bible Verses

WHAT CAN I RESEARCH DEEPER?

_____
_____
_____
_____

Thoughts

_____
_____
_____
_____

SONGS SANG

1. _____
2. _____
3. _____
4. _____
5. _____
6. _____

QUESTIONS

_____
_____
_____
_____
_____
_____
_____

SERMON NOTES...

WHAT IS GOD TELLING ME?

HOW CAN I APPLY
THIS TO MY LIFE?

Date

_____

TODAY'S PREACHER

_____

TODAY WE ARE FOCUSING ON THE...

☐ OLD TESTAMENT   ☐ NEW TESTAMENT

Prayer Requests

_____
_____
_____
_____
_____
_____
_____
_____
_____
_____

And the Lord, he it is that doth go before thee, he will be with thee, he will not fail thee, neither forsake thee, fear not, neither be dismayed.

Deuteronomy 31:8

Today's Sermon is About

_____
_____
_____
_____
_____
_____

1. _____
2. _____
3. _____
4. _____
5. _____

Bible Verses

WHAT CAN I
RESEARCH DEEPER?

_____
_____
_____
_____
_____

Thoughts

_____
_____
_____
_____

SONGS SANG

1. _____
2. _____
3. _____
4. _____
5. _____
6. _____

QUESTIONS

_____
_____
_____
_____
_____
_____

SERMON NOTES...

WHAT IS GOD TELLING ME?

HOW CAN I APPLY THIS TO MY LIFE?

Date

_____

TODAY'S PREACHER

_____

TODAY WE ARE FOCUSING ON THE...

☐ OLD TESTAMENT   ☐ NEW TESTAMENT

Prayer Requests

_____
_____
_____
_____
_____
_____
_____
_____
_____
_____
_____

Jesus Christ the same yesterday, and to day, and for ever.

Hebrews 13:8

Today's Sermon is About

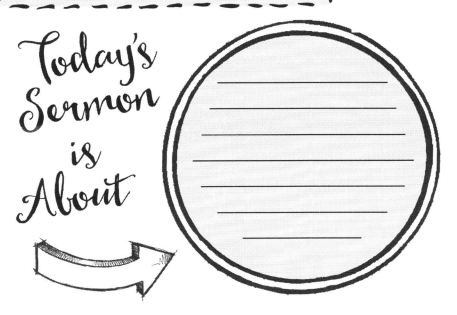

1. _____
2. _____
3. _____
4. _____
5. _____

Bible Verses

WHAT CAN I RESEARCH DEEPER?

_____
_____
_____
_____

Thoughts

_____
_____
_____

SONGS SANG

1. _____
2. _____
3. _____
4. _____
5. _____
6. _____

QUESTIONS

_____
_____
_____
_____
_____
_____

SERMON NOTES...

WHAT IS GOD TELLING ME?

HOW CAN I APPLY
THIS TO MY LIFE?

Date

_____

TODAY'S PREACHER

_____

TODAY WE ARE FOCUSING ON THE...

☐ OLD TESTAMENT   ☐ NEW TESTAMENT

Prayer Requests

_____
_____
_____
_____
_____
_____
_____
_____
_____
_____

These things I have spoken unto you, that in me ye might have peace. In the world ye shall have tribulation: but be of good cheer; I have overcome the world.

John 16:33

Today's Sermon is About

1. _____
2. _____
3. _____
4. _____
5. _____

Bible Verses

WHAT CAN I RESEARCH DEEPER?
_____
_____
_____
_____

Thoughts
_____
_____
_____
_____

SONGS SANG

1. _____
2. _____
3. _____
4. _____
5. _____
6. _____

QUESTIONS
_____
_____
_____
_____
_____
_____

SERMON NOTES...

WHAT IS GOD TELLING ME?

HOW CAN I APPLY THIS TO MY LIFE?

Date

_____

TODAY'S PREACHER

_____

TODAY WE ARE FOCUSING ON THE...

☐ OLD TESTAMENT ☐ NEW TESTAMENT

Prayer Requests

_____
_____
_____
_____
_____
_____
_____
_____
_____
_____

If we live in the Spirit, let us also walk in the Spirit.
Galatians 5:25

Today's Sermon is About

1. _____
2. _____
3. _____
4. _____
5. _____

Bible Verses

WHAT CAN I RESEARCH DEEPER?

_____
_____
_____
_____

Thoughts

_____
_____
_____
_____

SONGS SANG

1. _____
2. _____
3. _____
4. _____
5. _____
6. _____

QUESTIONS

_____
_____
_____
_____
_____
_____
_____

SERMON NOTES...

_____
_____
_____
_____
_____
_____
_____
_____
_____

WHAT IS GOD TELLING ME?

_____
_____
_____
_____
_____
_____
_____
_____
_____
_____

HOW CAN I APPLY THIS TO MY LIFE?

_____
_____
_____
_____
_____
_____
_____
_____
_____
_____

Date

_____

TODAY'S PREACHER

_____

TODAY WE ARE FOCUSING ON THE...

☐ OLD TESTAMENT   ☐ NEW TESTAMENT

Prayer Requests

_____
_____
_____
_____
_____
_____
_____
_____
_____
_____

Thou art all fair, my love; there is no spot in thee.

Song of Solomon 4:7

Today's Sermon is About

1. _____
2. _____
3. _____
4. _____
5. _____

Bible Verses

WHAT CAN I RESEARCH DEEPER?

_____
_____
_____
_____

Thoughts

_____
_____
_____
_____

SONGS SANG

1. _____
2. _____
3. _____
4. _____
5. _____
6. _____

QUESTIONS

_____
_____
_____
_____
_____
_____

SERMON NOTES...

WHAT IS GOD TELLING ME?

HOW CAN I APPLY THIS TO MY LIFE?

Date

_____

TODAY'S PREACHER

_____

TODAY WE ARE FOCUSING ON THE...

☐ OLD TESTAMENT ☐ NEW TESTAMENT

Prayer Requests

_____
_____
_____
_____
_____
_____
_____
_____
_____
_____

For the Lord of hosts hath purposed, and who shall disannul it? and his hand is stretched out, and who shall turn it back?

Isaiah 14:27

Today's Sermon is About

1. _____
2. _____
3. _____
4. _____
5. _____

Bible Verses

WHAT CAN I
RESEARCH DEEPER?

_____
_____
_____
_____

Thoughts

_____
_____
_____
_____

SONGS SANG

1. _____
2. _____
3. _____
4. _____
5. _____
6. _____

QUESTIONS

_____
_____
_____
_____
_____
_____

SERMON NOTES...

WHAT IS GOD TELLING ME?

HOW CAN I APPLY THIS TO MY LIFE?

Date
_____

TODAY'S PREACHER

_____

TODAY WE ARE FOCUSING ON THE...

☐ OLD TESTAMENT ☐ NEW TESTAMENT

Prayer Requests
_____
_____
_____
_____
_____
_____
_____
_____
_____
_____

For the vision is yet for an appointed time, but at the end it shall speak, and not lie: though it tarry, wait for it; because it will surely come, it will not tarry.

Habakkuk 2:3

Today's Sermon is About

1. _____
2. _____
3. _____
4. _____
5. _____

Bible Verses

WHAT CAN I
RESEARCH DEEPER?

_____
_____
_____

Thoughts

_____
_____
_____
_____

SONGS SANG

1. _____
2. _____
3. _____
4. _____
5. _____
6. _____

QUESTIONS

_____
_____
_____
_____
_____

SERMON NOTES...

WHAT IS GOD TELLING ME?

HOW CAN I APPLY THIS TO MY LIFE?

Date

_____

TODAY'S PREACHER

_____

TODAY WE ARE FOCUSING ON THE...

☐ OLD TESTAMENT   ☐ NEW TESTAMENT

Prayer Requests

_____
_____
_____
_____
_____
_____
_____
_____
_____
_____
_____

Strength and honour are her clothing; and she shall rejoice in time to come.

Proverbs 31:25

Today's Sermon is About

Bible Verses

1. _____
2. _____
3. _____
4. _____
5. _____

WHAT CAN I RESEARCH DEEPER?

_____
_____
_____
_____

Thoughts

_____
_____
_____
_____

SONGS SANG

1. _____
2. _____
3. _____
4. _____
5. _____
6. _____

QUESTIONS

_____
_____
_____
_____
_____
_____

SERMON NOTES...

WHAT IS GOD TELLING ME?

HOW CAN I APPLY THIS TO MY LIFE?

Date

_____

TODAY'S PREACHER

_____

TODAY WE ARE FOCUSING ON THE...

☐ OLD TESTAMENT   ☐ NEW TESTAMENT

Prayer Requests

_____
_____
_____
_____
_____
_____
_____
_____
_____

Let the word of Christ dwell in you richly in all wisdom; teaching and admonishing one another in psalms and hymns and spiritual songs, singing with grace in your hearts to the Lord.
Colossians 3:16

Today's Sermon is About

_____
_____
_____
_____
_____

1. _____
2. _____
3. _____
4. _____
5. _____

Bible Verses

WHAT CAN I RESEARCH DEEPER?

_____
_____
_____
_____

Thoughts

_____
_____
_____
_____

SONGS SANG

1. _____
2. _____
3. _____
4. _____
5. _____
6. _____

QUESTIONS

_____
_____
_____
_____
_____
_____

SERMON NOTES...

WHAT IS GOD TELLING ME?

HOW CAN I APPLY THIS TO MY LIFE?

About the Author:

After two years as a social media assistant, Madison Schacht makes her debut in the book industry. Her creativity, and outstanding eye for design is what separates her from the crowd.

With a love for Jesus and passion for music, she ministers on the worship team at her church.

About the Author:

Darlene Schacht is known by her readers as The Time-Warp Wife. She is an Evangelical Christian whose number one priority is to serve Jesus Christ in every area of her life. She and her husband Michael live in Manitoba Canada. Married 26 years, they have four children (three still at home) and a pug.

She's an award winning and New York Times best-selling author.

Find Darlene on the web here:

Blog: TimeWarpWife.com Facebook: timewarpwife

Twitter: timewarpwife Pinterest: timewarpwife

If you enjoyed this book, please leave a review at Amazon. Thank you!

Made in the USA
San Bernardino, CA
25 February 2016